Annie's Awesome Terrible Troublesome Hair

By Patty Grum and Margaret Solberg

Illustrated by Brigid Malloy

Y0-AQR-522

Annie was afraid of scissors.

So, who thought this was a good idea?

Annie clearly didn't.

This wasn't gonna happen.

NO WAY.

NO HOW.

So month after month,

    year after year,

        little Annie's hair GREW.

Way past her ears.

Way past her elbows.

Way past her fanny.

Way past her ANKLES!

That's when the trouble began.

First, there was The Violent Velcro Snag Event.

Then, there was The OH GOOD GRIEF, You Vacuumed Up My Hair Day!

Annie tried to face her fear again.

But the memories kept returning.

This wasn't gonna happen.

NO WAY.

NO HOW.

The trouble continued the day of the family hike.

Annie's hair swept the ENTIRE forest floor.

Oh, and that SUPER embarrasing Zipper Incident.

Poor Annie

Poor Susie

And the trouble continued.

There was The Gooey Chewy Bubble Gum Kapooey Day.

Mom dragged Annie to another salon.

Those scissors are dangerous. You've told me over and over.

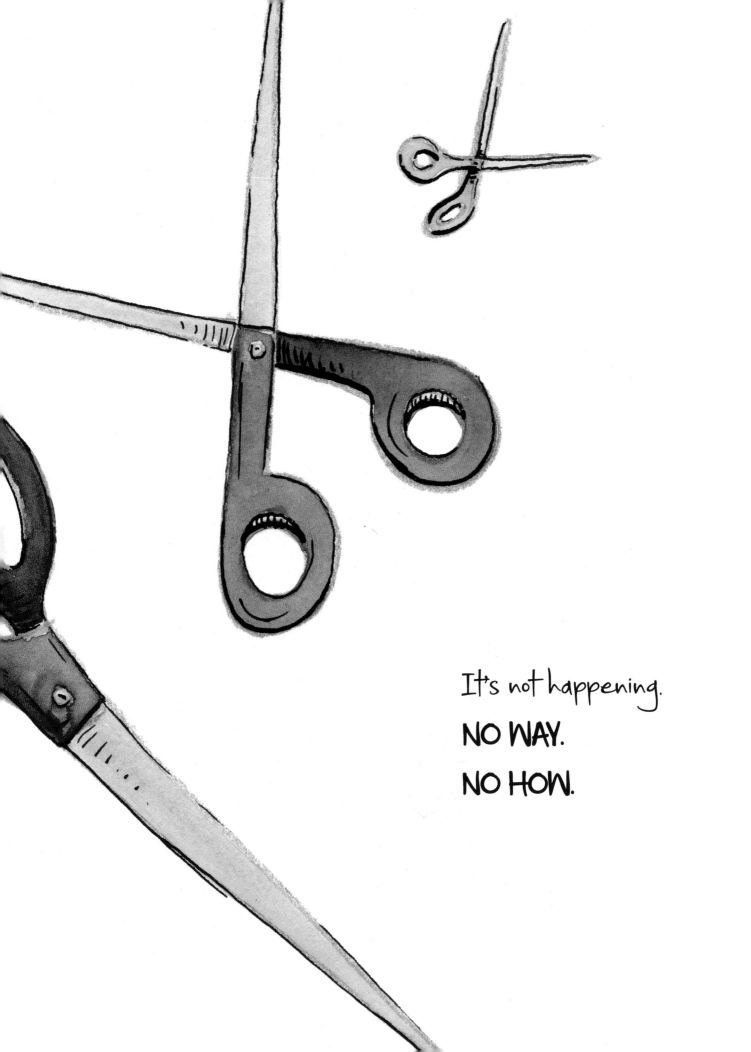

It's not happening.
NO WAY.
NO HOW.

However, Annie finally met her match on The Glittery Blue Slime Day. There was NO remedy.

It was the final straw.

"Enough!", said Annie. "My hair keeps getting me in trouble.

I am sick of it!
I must be brave.
I must be TOUGH!
I surrender, Mom. CUT MY HAIR!

P L E A S E ? ?

And so, it happened. Some way. Some how. Annie's hair is still awesome. Just less troublesome.

THE END

Margaret, Patty and Brigid would love to thank all the "Annies" in the world that have donated their hair to those without any. What a simple, easy gift to help bring a smile to those in need!

How to Make Your Own Crazy Hair Picture

First, have all the supplies ready.

Draw a hairless head on cardstock paper with crayons including the neck and shoulders. Color it with bright colors.

Put a few big drops of water in each color you want to use. Let the paint pallet sit for a few minutes with water in it.

Take the paintbrush and dribble a few drops of paint around the hairline of the picture.

Take the short straw and put it really close to the drop and start blowing really hard. Keep blowing all the extensions of the paint until they stop.

Repeat step #5 as many times as desired with many colors.

Let it completely dry.

Enjoy and frame it!

1 sturdy white piece of paper (cardstock)

box of crayons

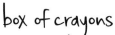

short straw about 5 inches long

cup of water

pallet of water colors with a paint brush

Check the back cover for an example of The Crazy Hair Picture.